Mind-Bending Challenging Logic Puzzles

Lagoon Books, London

Editor: Heather Dickson
Puzzle compilers: Des MacHale, Jenny Lynch,
Alison Crann, Hazel Richardson
Additional contributors: Lorna O'Connell,
Rosie Atkins, Jennifer Steele
Cover, design and illustrations: Linley Clode

Published by:
LAGOON BOOKS
PO BOX 311, KT2 5QW, UK

ISBN: 1899712240

© LAGOON BOOKS, 1997

Printed in Singapore.

MIND-BENDING
CHALLENGING LOGIC
PUZZLES

LAGOON
BOOKS

OTHER TITLES AVAILABLE FROM LAGOON BOOKS:

MIND-BENDING PUZZLE BOOKS

Mind-Bending Lateral Thinking Puzzles
ISBN 1899712062

More Mind-Bending Lateral Thinking Puzzles - Volume II
ISBN 1899712194

Mind-Bending Lateral Thinking Puzzles by Des MacHale
ISBN 1899712232

Mind-Bending Conundrums and Puzzles
ISBN 1899712038

Mind-Bending Classic Logic Puzzles
ISBN 1899712186

Mind-Bending Classic Word Puzzles
ISBN 1899712054

Mind-Bending Crossword Puzzles
ISBN 1899712399

All books can be ordered from bookshops by quoting the above ISBN numbers.
Some titles may not be available in all countries. All titles are available in the UK.

Introduction

Designed to test your
powers of deduction,
determination and
diligence, the cryptic
codes, conundrums and
sequence puzzles in
this book are guaranteed
to provide hours of fun,
as you battle to work
out the answers.

The solutions are at the
back of the book, but
don't be tempted to look
too soon – the richest
rewards come to those
who persevere!

1

The ages of Ann and Bill now add up to 91. Ann is now three times as old as Bill was at the time when Ann was twice as old as Bill is now. How old are Ann and Bill now?

Which number is two numbers to the left of the number which is two numbers to the right of the number which is three numbers to the right of the number which is two to the left of the number immediately to the right of the number 4?

123456789

At what time between 1pm and 2pm do the minute hand and the hour hand of a clock coincide exactly?

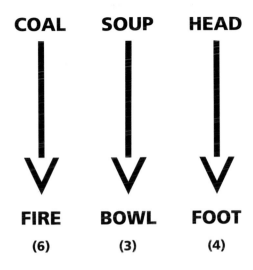

COAL   **SOUP**   **HEAD**

FIRE   **BOWL**   **FOOT**

(6)   **(3)**   **(4)**

Change each of the above words to the one below it, changing just one letter at a time and always forming a new word at each stage. To change cat to dog, for instance, you could go from cat to cot to cog (or dot) to dog. There is usually more than one way to make the changes, but the aim is to reach the second word in the fewest stages possible.

The numbers in brackets represent the minimum number of intermediate words.

5

QWERTY?

What is the next letter in this sequence?

Can you find five pieces of furniture in this grid? Choose a letter to start at and move one place up, down, left, right or diagonally to find the next. Each letter must only be used once, and all 25 letters must be used.

L	E	A	R	D
B	C	H	I	R
A	C	U	B	A
T	B	P	O	O
E	D	S	F	A

If the first three scales are balanced, what needs to be placed on the final set of scales? There are two possible solutions.

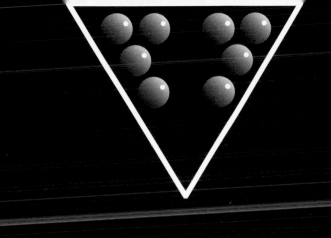

You are given eight snooker balls. Seven of these balls weigh exactly the same, but the eighth is marginally heavier. If you have a balance scale, how can you find the heavier ball in just two weighings?

$9 = P$ in the S S

Can you work out what the number and letters above really mean?

Can you find a single five-letter word which can be added to each of the following letters to make a series of six-letter words?

B

J

T

D

M

A rectangle sits in a quadrant of a circle with the indicated measurements. What is the length of the line **xy**?

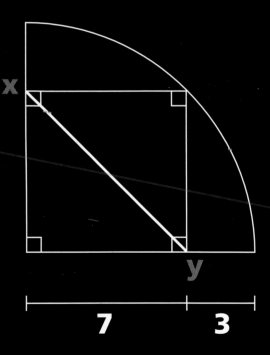

x

y

7   3

Alan, Betty and Colin were the children of a farmer. In his will, he left them his eleven horses; a half to Alan, a quarter to Betty and a sixth to Colin. As they were reluctant to cut up valuable livestock, they turned for advice to Old Jarvis, the village elder. What did he advise?

What number should be placed in the final square?

Seven friends hire a right-hand drive minibus for a day trip. There are two seats at the front, two behind and three at the back. John wants to drive, Mary doesn't want to sit near any of the men, Susan is sitting behind Sarah, and Paul - who has a bad neck and cannot turn around - can pass sweets to Gary, John and Sarah. Where is Andrew sitting?

Make the following correct with one stroke of the pen:

$$5 + 5 + 55 = 600$$

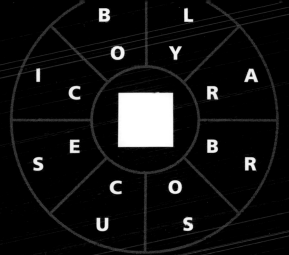

If you place the correct letter in the middle of this diagram, you can make a five-letter word from each straight line of letters. Can you find the letter and the words?

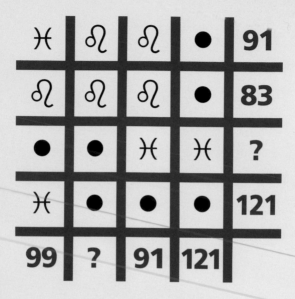

♓	♌	♌	●	91
♌	♌	♌	●	83
●	●	♓	♓	?
♓	●	●	●	121
99	?	91	121	

Each symbol has a numerical value and the totals of some of the columns and rows are shown. Can you work out the two missing totals?

Arrange the following set of tiles to form a number square so that the same five numbers which appear in row 1 also appear in the same order in column 1, the same numbers in row 2 also appear in column 2 etc.

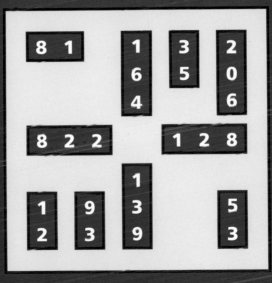

What number comes next in this sequence?

10,21,12,9,5,20, 13,25, 4,1,18,12,9,14,7,
9, 23,9,12,12, 2,5, 23,1,9,20,9,14,7,
6,15,18, 25,15,21, 2,25, 20,8,5,
3,12,15,3,11,20,15,23,5,18, 20,15,14,9,7,8,20,
1,20, G,16,13, 23,5, 23,9,12,12, 18,21,14,
1,23,1,25, 20,15, 18,15,13,5,

25,15,21,18,19, 1,19, 1,12,23,1,25,19,

18,15,13,5,15,

One morning Lord Capulet went to wake his
daughter Juliet, but found her room empty
except for this note, which appeared to be in
some sort of code. Sick with worry, he offered a
large amount of treasure to anyone who could
read it. Can you help him find her?

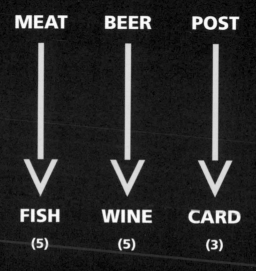

Change each of the above words to the one below it, changing just one letter at a time and always forming a new word at each stage. The numbers in brackets represent the minimum number of intermediate words.

Arrange the following set of tiles to form a number square so that the same five numbers which appear in row 1 also appear in the same order in column 1, the same numbers in row 2 also appear in column 2 etc.

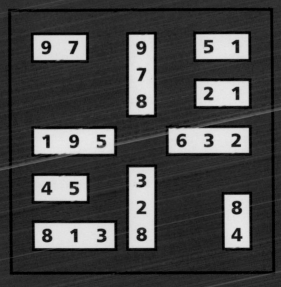

Can you work out what the number and letters below really mean ?

2400 =

KM of the G W of C

There was a go-slow at the airport, so we had time to buy a fluffy purple nylon donkey; Emma'd ridden the real thing on the beach. When we got back, Mum said she'd pop a risotto in the oven.

In this extract from her essay about the holidays, Lucy has hidden the names of four of the cities she visited with her family. Can you find them?

What number should be placed in the final circle?

In a darts competition each dart scores either 40, 39, 24, 23, 17 or 16 points. How many darts must be thrown to score exactly 100 points?

An arch is in the form of a circle with a straight line base. If the width of the base is 16 feet, and the height of the arch is 6 feet at its maximum, what is the radius of the whole circle?

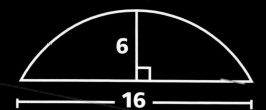

a) **Peril in Eden.** *(6)*

b) **Gaze at local tax demand.** *(5)*

c) **Dog on the road startles examiner.**
   (6, three words)

d) **Call someone with an average
   amount of hair.** *(4, three words)*

e) **Cad may answer back.** *(6)*

f) **Poet eats this for a bet.**
   (5, three words)

The clues above will give you a series of
words which are anagrams of each other.
The number in brackets tells you the number of
letters in the words. For example, this instrument
emits a cry of pain (5) - ORGAN; GROAN.

L,15,30,40,A,?

What comes next in this sequence?

Using each of the ten digits shown below, only once, find two five-digit numbers with the largest possible product.

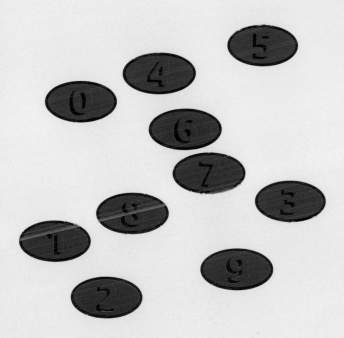

Daniel is moving house and needs to move his pets as well as his belongings. His car is so packed with furniture that he can only take one pet at a time, but this presents a problem. He owns a dog, a cat and a tank of fish. If left alone with the cat, the dog will certainly chase it; if the cat is left alone with the fish, it may well try to eat them. How many trips must Daniel make to ensure that all his pets reach their new home safely?

Arrange the above set of tiles to form a number square so that the numbers in each column and row add up to 30.

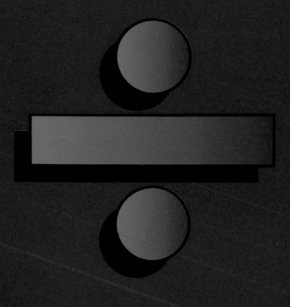

There is a certain number, less than 3000, which when divided by 2 leaves a remainder of 1, by 3 a remainder of 2, by 4 a remainder of 3, by 5 a remainder of 4, by 6 a remainder of 5, by 7 a remainder of 6, by 8 a remainder of 7, by 9 a remainder of 8 and by 10 a remainder of 9! What is this number?

Can you find a three-letter word which will fit the spaces below to make five new words?

M _ _ _ N

C _ _ _ T

S _ _ _ CE

H _ _ _ S

P _ _ _ ED

Which is the closer fit, a square peg in a round hole or a round peg in a square hole?

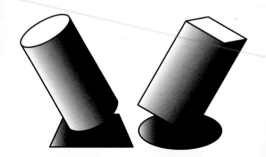

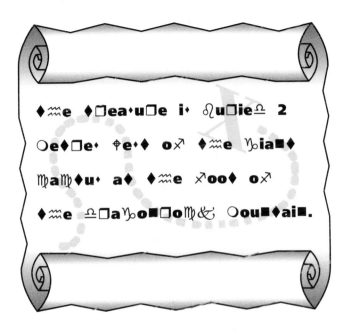

Two brothers Henry and Harry couldn't believe their eyes when they found this drawing of what looked like a treasure map, while on holiday with their parents in America's Wild West. Unfortunately, they couldn't read the writing, which seemed to be in some sort of code. Can you help them to decipher it?

TALE	COVE	HAVE
BRIE	SIDE	CAP
LAZE	SETTER	QUIT

VILE	HOSE	BLOW
LOSE	FOLLY	OLD
BATS	BOY	CLAP

COT	LIE	HEART	SNIP
PINT	NEW	EDGE	HAD
TRY	TRACED	LATER	CHAT

Find the letter which can be added to all three words, in any position, to make three new words. When you have found all the letters, rearrange them to give the title of a book.

Make the following correct with one stroke of the pen:

$$101010 = 9.50$$

If a number consisting of three different digits is subtracted from its reverse, the answer is the same three digits in yet another order.
What is the number?

18 = H on a G C

Can you work out what the number and letters above really mean?

Susan, Stephen and Stephanie helped their mother to carry the shopping home. Each child had seven pieces of fruit in his or her bag, a mixture of apples and oranges. Stephanie had twice as many apples as Susan and less oranges than Stephen. Stephen had half as many oranges as Susan. How many apples did he have?

Each symbol has a numerical value and the totals of some of the columns and rows are shown. Can you work out the two missing totals?

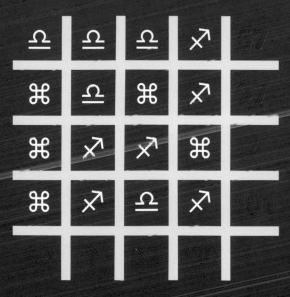

A woman is offered a 10% decrease in her weekly wage one week, followed by an immediate 11% increase to her wage the week after. Should she accept the offer?

A, A, A, A, ?

Which letter comes next in this sequence?

SWAN		OVAL
NONE		BELL
ARTS		SPAR
SLOW		INCH
TARN		LIMP
PLAY		BOAT
PICK		STEM

Change the second letter of each word to the left and right of the central column. Put the letter used in the middle. When the central column is correctly filled in, another word can be read downwards.

Can you arrange seven coins in six rows so that there will be exactly three coins in each row?

Place the numbers 1, 2, 3, 4, 5, 6, 7, 8, 9 along the sides of a triangle so that the numbers along each side add up to the same total and that total is as large as possible.

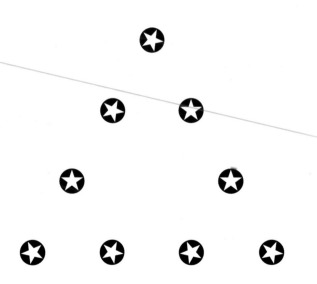

(a) The hard worker won't linger! *(6)*

(b) Notice the crockery slip, and prevent it falling. *(4, three words)*

(c) He rearranged his luggage and marched off, determined to reach the next county that evening. *(6, three words)*

(d) The bishop's hat is not in my area of responsibility, and nor is winding the clock, whatever it may be worth. *(5, four words)*

(e) Androcles managed to pacify the lion - though not by giving it food - and found that it was a good friend to have on his side. *(4, four words)*

> The clues above will give you a series of words which are anagrams of each other.
> The number in brackets tells you the number of letters in the words. For example, an object found in the dark *(5)* - THING; NIGHT.

A farmer plants potatoes for his own use and to grow seed for next year's crop. If the yield is exactly ten times the amount planted and he uses ten tons of potatoes every year, what is the minimum weight of potatoes he should plant now?

Which number comes next in this sequence?

20, 1, 18, 4, 13, 6, 10, 15, ?

You find this nameplate on a tomb that you know belongs to a pharaoh. You know how the Egyptians wrote certain letters:

H = ▼   L = ↑

From the above, can you find out who was buried in the tomb with this inscription?

AAEILNNNPSVY *(12)*

AACHILNNOORRT *(5, 8)*

AEIMNNOST *(9)*

CIINNOSSW *(9)*

AEEHHIMNPRSW *(3, 9)*

AAIILNOSU *(9)*

Unscramble the above sets of letters to find words which all have something in common - what is it?

8 = N in an O

Can you work out what the number and letters above really mean ?

The first four sets of scales balance.
What symbols need to be added to the final
set of scales to achieve a similar equilibrium?

When Archie is twice as old as he is now, he will be four times as old as he was six years ago. How old is Archie?

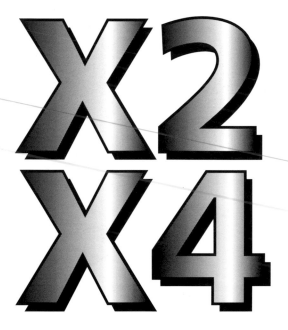

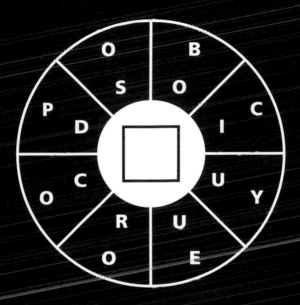

If you place the correct letter in the middle of this diagram, you can make a five-letter word from each straight line of letters. Can you find the letter and the words?

F...A...X
T...R...A...N...S...M...I...S...S...I...O...N

TOP SECRET

GS5 G1IT5G U15I G15M9TSG'H
N9HH915M 9H GS5 PTY
1T5MG H5IT59 H5IT59E9GXS

W15 M15G U19O
T1515W O21XP
N

The CIA was confident that no civilian would be able to crack its highly sophisticated and top secret code, but after receiving the following fax, Agent X was not so sure. Can you work out what it says?

How can you divide twelve in half and get seven?

Karen has been dating four men and all of them have asked to see her on Friday night. She has agreed to see them all for an hour each, and arranged to meet each of them in the same bar. Richard and Jonathan know one another. Jonathan and Darren both know Tim, but not each other. All of the men have jobs in bars or clubs which means they have to work on a Friday evening. Richard has to go to work earlier than Tim, but not as early as Darren. What order should Karen see them in so as not to get found out, or cause any arguments between friends?

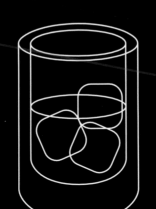

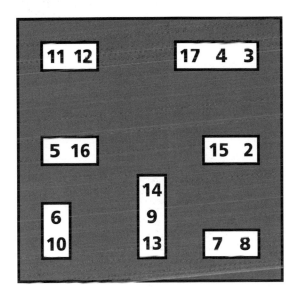

Arrange the above set of tiles to form a number square so that the numbers in each column and row add up to 38.

STRONG • DEPRESSION

HUE • TARNISH

FISH • CAPER

ACHING • CUPBOARD

ANCIENT • FROZEN

LABYRINTH • GRAIN

WHEELED VEHICLE • OMISSION SIGN

REIMBURSE • DRAMA

The above clues will give you pairs of words that differ by the inclusion of only one letter. This extra letter should fit in the shaded box in each answer. When you have solved all the clues, rearrange these letters to give the name of a musical instrument.

Using 10 coins with face values of 1p, 2p, 5p, 10p, 20p and 50p, what is the largest amount of money you could have and not be able to make up £1 (=100p) exactly?

Can you work out what the number and letters below really mean?

206 = B in the HB

How can you make 100 using six nines only?

There is a ten-letter word in this diagram; the letters are in order, but mixed up with some red herrings. Starting with the central P, can you find the word?

What number should be placed in the final triangle?

If A and B are the centre points of adjacent faces of a cubic box and O is a vertex of the box common to both faces, how big is the angle AOB?

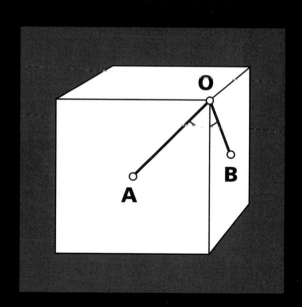

R, O, Y, G, B, I, ?

What letter completes this sequence?

11

How would you write eleven thousand and eleven hundred and eleven?

Using the numbers 1, 5, 6 and 7 once and only once make up 21.

There is a relationship between the rows of numbers in this square. Can you work out what it is and so find the missing number?

a 8	5	9	7	4
b 5	1	8	2	2
c 3	4	1	5	?
d 7	6	2	8	5
e 4	2	1	3	3

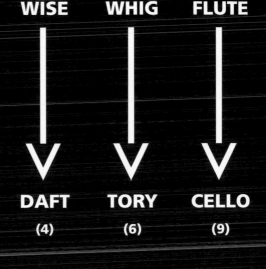

WISE	WHIG	FLUTE
∨	∨	∨
DAFT	**TORY**	**CELLO**
(4)	(6)	(9)

Change each of the above words to the one below it, changing just one letter at a time and always forming a new word at each stage. The numbers in brackets represent the minimum number of intermediate words.

108 = E in the PT

Can you work out what the number and letters above really mean?

How can you tell, without any means of measurement, if an open cylindrical glass containing water is more than half full?

Can you find five collective nouns in this grid? Choose a letter to start at and move one place up, down, left, right or diagonally to find the next. Each letter must only be used once, and all 25 letters must be used.

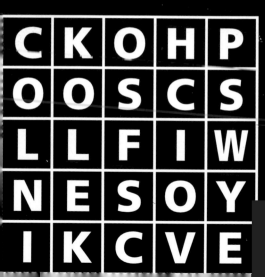

C	K	O	H	P
O	O	S	C	S
L	L	F	I	W
N	E	S	O	Y
I	K	C	V	E

114 = C in the K

Can you work out what the number and letters above really mean?

Mr Jones drove his car up a hill for half a mile at 30 miles an hour. How fast would he have to drive his car back down the hill to average 60 miles an hour for the whole journey?

A guard at Stone Island Prison found prisoner 1295 trying to pass the following note under the table to his visitor. Fearing it might be something to do with a possible break-out, the guard confiscated the piece of paper but cannot work out what it says on it. Can you read the message and help him to avert a potential disaster?

TH?T+NN!L$SN?5RLYF£N

$SH&D. W!7R?W9$T£NGF{RTH&N!

WM((NWH?NTH?G=9RDSW%LL

N[TS!?-S. B&TH!R&T(P$CK+S-PW$

THTH&M[N?Y.

There are three relationships between the columns of figures in this grid. Can you work out what they are?

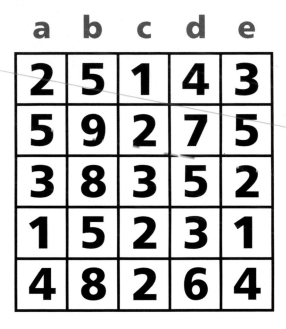

a	b	c	d	e
2	5	1	4	3
5	9	2	7	5
3	8	3	5	2
1	5	2	3	1
4	8	2	6	4

1760 = Y in a M

Can you work out what the number and letters above really mean?

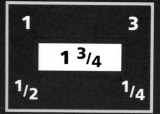

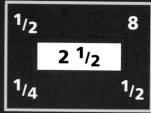

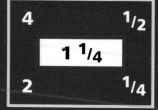

What number should be placed in the final rectangle?

Change the second letter of each word to the left and right of the central column. Put the letter used in the middle. When the central column is correctly filled in, another word can be read downwards.

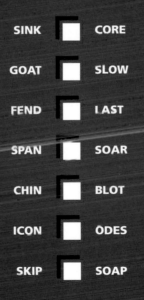

SINK	U	CORE
GOAT	N	SLOW
FEND	I	LAST
SPAN	C	SOAR
CHIN	O	BLOT
ICON	R	ODES
SKIP	N	SOAP

solutions

1. Ann is 63, Bill is 28.
   Use equations:
   $A + B = 91$
   $A = 3(B - x)$
   $2B = A - x$

2. Six.

3. 1/11 of an hour after 1pm.

4.
COAL	SOUP	HEAD
COAT	SOUL	HELD
COST	SOIL	HOLD
CAST	BOIL	HOLT
CASE	BOWL	HOOT
CARE		FOOT
FARE		
FIRE		

5. U (top row of letters on a keyboard).

6. Chair, table, sofa, cupboard, bed.

7. Either add one extra lemon OR two pineapples.

8. Divide the balls into three groups of sizes three, three and two. Weigh the two groups of three against each other on the scales. If: **a)** one group is heavier than the other, it must contain the heavier ball. Pick the heavier group, and weigh any two of them against each other. If one is heavier than the other, you have found the heavier ball; if they balance, then the third of the group must be the heavy ball. **b)** the two groups of three balance, the heavy ball must be one of the two remaining balls. Weigh these two remaining balls and find the heavier one.

9. There are 9 planets in the solar system.

10. The word is 'angle' (bangle, dangle, jangle, mangle, tangle).

11. $xy = OB = 7 + 3 = 10$.

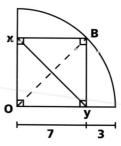

12. Old Jarvis puts his old nag with the other horses to make twelve. Six are given to Alan (a half), three are given to Betty (a quarter) and two are given to Colin (a sixth). Now $6 + 3 + 2 = 11$ - the number of horses which belonged to their father, so Jarvis can take back his old nag

and everyone is happy.

13. 47.

The sequence is $(a + b) \times c - d = e$

14. Andrew is sitting on the back seat, two behind the front passenger.

15. 545 + 55 = 600.

16. K (lucky, rakes, brick, books).

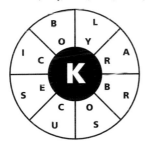

17. The missing column total is 98, the missing row total is 114.

$\maltese = 25$, $\bullet = 32$, $\Omega = 17$

18.

1	2	1	3	9
2	0	6	5	3
1	6	4	8	1
3	5	8	2	2
9	3	1	2	8

19. 5 (they are the start and end dates of the two World Wars).

20. Juliet my darling I will be waiting for you by the clocktower tonight at 7pm We will run away to Rome Yours as always Romeo

Code: Each letter is written as its corresponding number in the the alphabet:

1	2	3	4	5	6	7	8	9	10	11	12	13
A	B	C	D	E	F	G	H	I	J	K	L	M

14	15	16	17	18	19	20	21	22	23	24	25	26
N	O	P	Q	R	S	T	U	V	W	X	Y	Z

solutions

21.

MEAT	BEER	POST
MELT	BEES	PORT/COST
MALT	BETS	PART/CAST
MAST	BITS	CART
FAST	WITS	CARD
FIST	WINS	
FISH	WINE	

22.

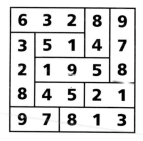

23. There are 2400 kilometres of the Great Wall of China.

24. *There was a go-slow at the airport, so we had time to buy a fluffy purple nylon donkey; Emma'd ridden the real thing on the beach. When we got back, Mum said she'd pop a risotto in the oven.*

25. 30. The sequence is
$$((d \div c) + b) \times a = e$$

26. Six. Four darts scoring 17 each = 68, plus two darts scoring 16 each = 32 = 100.

27. The radius of the circle is 8.3 feet.

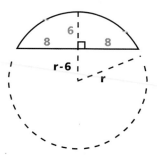

Theorem of Pythagoras = The square of the hypotenuse on a right-angled triangle is equal to the sum of the squares of the other two sides. So:

$r^2 = 8^2 + (r - 6)^2$

$r^2 = 64 + r^2 - 12r + 36$

$12r = 100$

$r = 100 / 12$

$= 8 \frac{1}{3}$

28. (a) danger / garden

   (b) stare / rates

   (d) setter / street / tester

   (e) name / mean / mane

   (f) rotter / retort

   (c) Keats / steak / stake

29. G for game

   (points in a game of tennis).

30. 96420 x 87531 = 8439739020.

31. Seven trips. First he takes the cat to his new home, then goes back to collect the fish. He leaves the fish in the new house and takes the cat back with him to the old house, where he leaves it again. He then takes the dog and leaves it with the fish. Finally he collects the cat from his old house, takes it to the new one, and all three pets are safe.

32.

12	3	1	14
6	8	12	4
11	5	4	10
1	14	13	2

33. 2519.

34. OUR.

35. A square peg in a round hole takes up about 64% of the area, whereas a round peg in a square hole takes up about 78% of the area, so the round peg in a square hole is a tighter fit.

36. The treasure is buried 2 metres west of the giant cactus at the foot of the dragonrock mountain.

Code: the vowels and numbers are the same, but the consonants have been replaced with symbols.

37. The letters in order of appearance are: B, L, E, O, U, S, A, K, H, E, and the book is Bleak House.

38. 10T010 = 9.50.

39. One possibility is:
954 - 459 = 495.

40. 18 is the number of holes on a golf course.

41. Five. Susan had three apples and four oranges. Stephen had five apples and two oranges. Stephanie had six apples and one orange.

42. The missing column total is 86, the missing row total is 116.

♎ = 12, ⌘ = 27, ⚐ = 31

43. No, she should not accept the offer. If, for example, she was earning £100 per week, she would earn £90 in the first week, if she took a 10% cut. The following week, after an 11% rise, she would earn only £99.90 (£90 + 11% of £90).

44. E (they are all continents).

45. PICTURE.

46. Yes. (see diagram below)

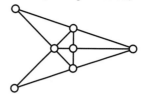

47. The largest equal sum you can have along each side is 23.

48.
(a) toiler / loiter
(b) spot / pots / stop
(c) sorted / strode / Dorset
(d) mitre / remit / timer / merit
(e) tame / meat / mate / team

49. He must plant 1 1/9 tons.

50. 2 (they are numbers on a dartboard, moving clockwise from 20).

51. The top nameplate says 'pharaoh', the second says 'cleopatra' (see opposite).

H O A R A H P
↓ α λ ∿ λ ↓ 𝔜

C L E O P A T R A
△ ╛ ⊖ α 𝔜 λ H ∿ λ

52. They are all American states: Pennsylvania, North Carolina, Minnesota, Wisconsin, New Hampshire and Louisiana.

53. There are 8 notes in an octave.

54. ○❖
□ = 8, ❖ = 2, ○ = 5, ◆ = 3.

55. 12 years old.

56. M (broom, mouse, comic, dumpy).

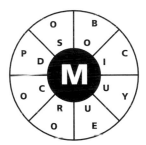

57. THE TARGET FOR TONIGHT'S MISSION IS THE KGB AGENT SERGEI SERGEIVITCH DO NOT FAIL GOOD LUCK M

Code: the consonants are written using the corresponding letter of the reversed alphabet, the vowels are written as their number in the alphabet.

58. Use roman numerals.

$$XII = 12$$
$$XII = 7$$

59. Jonathan, Darren, Richard, Tim.

60.

17	4	3	14
6	11	12	9
10	7	8	13
5	16	15	2

solutions

61. The letters in the shaded boxes form the word **CLARINET**.

TOUGH   T**R**OUGH
TINT   T**A**INT
DACE   DA**N**CE
SORE   S**T**ORE
OLD   **C**OLD
MAZE   MA**I**ZE
CART   CAR**E**T
PAY   P**L**AY

62. £1.43. (1 x 50p, 4 x 20p, 4 x 2p, 1 x 5p).

63. There are 206 bones in the human body.

64. 99 + (99 ÷ 99) = 100.

65. PERFECTION.

66. 10. The sequence is

$(c + a) \times d - b = e$.

67. Produce OA to X, OB to Y then OX = OY = XY so AOB = 60°.

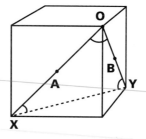

68. V for violet (colours of the rainbow).

69. 11,000 + 1,100 + 11 = 12,111.

70. 6 ÷ (1 - (5 ÷ 7)) = 21.

71. The missing number is 2 (a - b = c and d - e = c).

72.

WISE	WHIG	FLUTE
WIRE	WHIP	FLUME
DIRE	CHIP	FLUMP
DARE	CHIN	SLUMP
DART	COIN	SLUMS
DAFT	CORN	SLAMS

```
TORN    SEAMS
TORY    SEALS
        SELLS
        CELLS
        CELLO
```

73. There are 108 elements in the periodic table.

74. Tilt the glass sideways so that the water level is horizontal. If it is more than half full, the water will overflow.

75. Flock, covey, school, skein, wisp.

76. There are 114 chapters in the Koran.

77. It doesn't matter what speed he travels at during the return leg, he cannot average 60 mph for the whole journey. To average 60 mph for a journey of 1/2 a mile plus 1/2 a mile (= 1 mile) would take one minute for the entire journey, but he has already used up that one minute in driving the 1/2 mile up the hill at 30 mph.

78. THE TUNNEL IS NEARLY FINISHED. WE ARE WAITING FOR THE NEW MOON WHEN THE GUARDS WILL NOT SEE US. BE THERE TO PICK US UP WITH THE MONEY.

Code: consonants stay the same, vowels have been substituted (see below). There are no spaces between words.

A is **5,7** or **9**
E is **!, ?** or **&**
I is **$, £** or **%**
O is **(, {** or **[**
U is **+, -** or **=**

79. a + 2 = d, d - e = c, c + d = b.

80. There are 1760 yards in a mile.

81. 4 ½

The sequence is b x (a - c) + d = e.

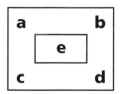

82. UNICORN.